BECOMING a

PRIESTHOOD MAN

BECOMING a

PRIESTHOOD MAN

The Parable of the celery and the Studebaker

How a broken dream in
The summer of 1948 changed a young man's life for the good.

George D. Durrant
with Heather Durrant

Becoming a Priesthood Man by George D. Durrant

August 2009

Names and personalities of the characters in this work of fiction were created soley in the imagination of the author. Resemblance to persons now living is entirely coincidental.

Published by:

Granite Publishing and Distribution, LLC
868 North 1430 West
Orem, UT 84057
(801) 229-9023 Toll Free (800) 574-5779
Fax (801) 229-1924

ISBN: 978-1-59936-044-7
Library of Congress Card Control Number: 2009932225

Printed in the United States of America 2009

DEDICATION

To my older brother Stewart A. Durrant and to my dear friend Delmar Fraughton. Both of them are my heroes in this book and in life.

FACT AND FICTION

A long time ago, I was your age. I was a priest in the Aaronic Priesthood.

I've tried to reach back into my memory and recall the events that happened to me in those days. Retrieving those memories would have enabled me to write this book. The problem is that those personal memories revealed that I was quite a boring young man! So to keep from putting you to sleep, I've added a few facts that didn't happen in exactly the way I describe them—things like the story of Lydia falling in love with me, and my confrontations with a bully.

However the feelings I had in those olden days, when I was becoming a young Priesthood Man, are accurately recorded. And all of the experiences included in this book are based on actual events.

So, with that in mind, please read on.

PREFACE

A PRIEST, IN THE AARONIC PRIESTHOOD, IS A YOUNG MAN OF GOD.

On November 14, 1947, I was ordained a Priest in the Aaronic Priesthood. In character, however, I wasn't a Priest, for I wasn't yet a young man of God.

The next summer, 1948, I had some great experiences which enabled me to understand more fully what becoming a young man of God entailed. It was during that summer that I began to be a young Priesthood Man.

Contents

During that Summer of 1948 I learned, that to become a priest and a priesthood man I had to…

BECOMING A PRIESTHOOD MAN

1. To become a priest I had to have a dream.

Hap Holmstead had been a star football player for the University of Utah. That was pretty impressive to an eleventh-grader like me. He didn't look much like a football player. He was bald-headed and a little overweight. Of course he had played twenty six years ago, on the 1922 team so I figured I could look past that. Hap was my favorite teacher. I think his athletic past was the reason he was my favorite. Sports were an important part of my life, and having a famous athlete teach my class was quite an honor. He taught the class "American Problems." I wasn't as interested in American Problems as I was in my own problems. I had plenty of those.

Lum Nelson, one of my best friends, and I were sitting in the back of the classroom eating pine nuts and talking about his new job down in the back of the city hall. Hap was trying to tell us about how Thomas Dewey was going beat Harry Truman in the upcoming presidential election. Lum and I didn't have much interest in stuff like that. When Hap saw us talking, he stopped and said, "You guys had better start listening or you'll end up spending the rest of your life working in a gas station."

I was shocked that he said that because that was exactly what I wanted to do when I graduated from high school. I liked to go to "Kelly's" gas station riding in my father's car and see Don Rutledge run from the little office and say, "You want her filled up, Bert?" Don was a dashing fellow, and he had a little Plymouth two seater that was bright red. He wasn't married and all the pretty girls wanted to go out with him. I wanted to be like him when I was his age. Thus, the dreams of a career in the petroleum business.

Hap then looked at me and said, "George, Gib Bachelor told me that you're a cousin to his wife Orpha." I didn't know who my cousins all were—I had about a thousand of them--and so I wasn't sure if he was right or wrong. Hap added, "Gib was telling me that he paid for the house he just finished building with the money that he made last summer growing celery. Did you know that he did that?" Hap asked looking right at me.

"No." I replied.

"Well he did," Hap answered. "He made a deal with Rulon Nichols. He did the work of growing the celery and Rulon provided the land and paid all the expenses. They both made six thousand dollars."

That caught my complete attention more than anything Hap had said in the months I had been in his class. "Six thousand dollars!" I thought to myself. I was shocked that anybody in American Fork could ever make six thousand dollars in one summer. That was enough to buy a new car, take a two week vacation to California, and still put three thousand dollars in the bank!

Hap continued talking about Harry Truman. I didn't hear what he said because I was thinking about celery and six thousand dollars.

* * * * *

It was a cold day in late March. It seemed like the wind blew every day in March. I liked the rain and the snow, but I couldn't see why Heavenly Father created wind. All it ever did was muss up my hair so that I looked like the twerp that Bobby Jackson said that I was. I hated Bobby Jackson and the way he bullied me. The wind made the cold air colder. I nearly froze to death as I walked across the football field, down the hill, past the Star Flour mill and up the Alpine Road to my house. When I got home I took off my coat and asked my mom, "Do you know Gib Bachelor?"

"Sure I do. He's married to your cousin Orpha," she replied.

"What does he do to earn a living?"

"He's a house painter."

"Does he grow celery?"

"I think he did that last summer as a part-time job. I think he made quite a bit of money. I know they just built a new house. Why do you ask?"

I didn't answer. I went out the side door of the house and I ran down the twelve steps that went into the cellar. I picked up two wire buckets and headed for the chicken coops to gather the eggs. I hated gathering eggs. I hated living on a chicken farm. I wished my dad owned a bakery like Leroy Griffin's dad did. That bakery was the sweetest smelling place in town, and my dad's chicken coops were the worst smelling place. But the task didn't seem so bad today. I counted the eggs as I took them from the nests and put them into the buckets. I counted to one hundred sixty-seven. I wondered how many buckets it would take to gather six thousand eggs. Wow! Six thousand dollars. Even two thousand dollars would be enough to buy a new car. With that kind of money I could buy a Studebaker—the most beautiful car ever developed by mankind. Man! If I had a Studebaker, I would be the most popular kid in high school. I would transform from eleventh grade dud to twelfth grade stud over the summer. American Fork High wouldn't know what had hit it!

The next morning I bounded out of bed like a wild bull I felt like I was headed for fame and riches. I hadn't been so filled with excitement since the week before when I walked into Thornton Drug and saw Lydia standing there with three other girls! She was dressed in a long grey coat. No movie star, even Betty Grable, ever looked half as good. When she spotted me, she smiled and said, "Hello George." I could tell she liked me by the way her voice sounded. It was kind of low and soothing. I couldn't reply because my heart threatened to burst open. I just walked away. At that moment, my excitement had dissipated and I felt like the twerp that Bobby Jackson called me every time he saw me. I hated him saying that, especially when others were around.

But all that was last week. This was now and I was going to make lots of money growing celery. In my mind, I could see Lydia opposite me riding along in the fanciest car in town—my own 1948 Studebaker. I could see the other girls watching us pass by and wishing they were Lydia.

BECOMING A PRIESTHOOD MAN

As I ate my Wheaties that morning I wondered how many little flakes were in the box. I would have counted them if I had the time. I reckoned there would be nowhere near six thousand of them. Then I got to wondering if I could really be a farmer. I didn't know much about growing crops. When I picked up the bowl to drink the last little bit of sweet milk the perfect idea hit me like a flash. Delmar Fraughton, my best friend, lived on a farm in Kamas before he moved to American Fork in the seventh grade. He knew about farming, harnessing horses, and driving trucks. He was American Fork High School's greatest athlete. He was a star in football and basketball, a guy who was as strong as an ox, as quick as a fox, and a guy who all the girls adored even if he didn't have a car. He would be the perfect partner in my quest to be a thousandaire!

Another good thing about Delmar was that he liked horses better than he liked cars. So I guessed he'd put his thousands into horses. I liked that idea because I didn't want any other kid to have a new car. I didn't want any competition in my quest to be the most preferred man on campus. After thinking about all of these things, I put on my coat and toboggan hat, and headed across the street to Delmar's house. I was about to form a winning partnership. I had a dream and the product of that dream was going to change everything.

Little did I know the problems that lie ahead.

2. To become a priest I had to commit to make my dream come true.

As we walked to school, I told Delmar about my idea. I didn't explain it very well because I was too excited to be logical. Finally, about the time we were passing the Star Flour Mill, he got the idea. I kept talking all the way down the mill lane. Then, as we crossed the foot bridge and started up the steep hill to the school, he finally caught the vision and a big smile came over his face. He liked what I was saying, but wondered who would ever agree to let us be share croppers on their land.

We arrived at the east door of the high school. Delmar headed off to algebra on the ground floor and I went up the stairs to my bookkeeping class. Mrs. Mortenson was my bookkeeping teacher. She was the nicest lady in the whole town. I could tell that she liked me, but she told me I should quit being so lazy. She said I should start paying attention in class and doing the bookkeeping problems I was supposed to do for homework. She talked about debits and credits, and I just never could tell the difference. That day in class I kept looking at her like I was paying attention. But she didn't know that I was thinking about $6000 dollars. Finally I raised my hand. She looked at me and asked, "What?"

I asked, "How could I find out the names of all the farmers in American Fork?"

"George, how does this relate to what we're talking about?" She asked.

I smiled and replied, "You're talking about money and I'm talking about money, too. A lot of money." I wanted to tell her about my six thousand dollars, but now wasn't the time.

She sighed, "Why don't you ask your brother Stewart. He's the county agent. He knows all the farmers. But for now, let's focus on balance sheets."

I didn't know Stewart was working with the farmers. He was the oldest in our family of eight children. I was the youngest. He was married, had two children, and was the Bishop of our ward. With so many things going on, we had never gotten around to talking about what he did for a living. This was the first I'd heard about Stewart the county agent. Mrs. Mortenson had saved the day!

That night, Stewart came up to our place to talk to Dad about a fishing trip they were planning. The moment I saw his car drive up, I ran outside to talk to him.

"Do you know all the farmers in American Fork?" I asked.

"Yeah I do," he replied. "Why do you ask that?"

"I was wondering who would be willing to let my friend Delmar and me be sharecroppers so we could grow some celery."

"You want to grow celery?" He asked skeptically. When I nodded, he continued, "Growing celery is a lot of work. Mom says that you don't like to do anything that requires much effort. She told me that your grades in school are terrible. She's really worried about you not being willing to work or be responsible."

I replied in a determined tone, "I would be willing to work if I was growing celery."

Stewart seemed a bit surprised at my answer and with the sincerity in my voice. He asked, "George, why didn't you come to church last Sunday? You're a priest now, but you sure don't act like it. You were supposed to administer at the sacrament table like you told me you would. But you didn't even show up."

"I was tired last Sunday and decided to tell Mom that I was sick," I replied. "Besides, I was there the week before. Church just isn't exciting anymore. But I'll try to be there next week."

"Mom told me she heard you talking to Delmar and some other guy while you were sitting on the porch. She said you swore a couple of times. It really hurt her feelings. She never thought you would swear."

I looked down at my feet and wished he would stop talking to me about that kind of stuff. I wanted to talk about who he thought would let us be sharecroppers.

I finally replied, "I didn't swear that much. Besides, the other guys talk that way. I just want to be one of them."

"Well, I don't know who the guys are, but you're not just one of them. You're a priest—a young man of God, but you sure don't act like one."

When he said that, I knew he was right. But it still made me mad. And what he said next made me want to go somewhere and cry.

"I'm not sure most farmers would want a guy working on their land who was lazy and who wasn't determined enough to take responsibility."

"I can take responsibility!" I said defensively.

"Well, they want someone they can trust. They want someone who keeps his promises. If they let you be a sharecropper they'd want to know that they could count on you."

"They could count on me." I nearly yelled.

Stewart's face softened, "Well, maybe they could. I love you, George. I don't want to be hard on you. But you can see what I'm talking about. It's time for you to grow up. I get the feeling that you're nearly ready to do that. I'll look around and see who would be interested. Are you planning on working alone?"

"No. Like I said, Delmar would be my partner."

Stewart then went out to the barn where Dad was fixing a broken fence so they could plan their fishing trip.

The next day, I told Delmar about what I had said to Stewart. He was really excited! "Your brother, Stewart, is about the best guy I have ever known. He sure is a good bishop. And he's real kind to my mother. If he's on our side, we are in business for sure."

That day in school I didn't swear at all, even though my friends were doing quite a bit of it. I only slipped a couple of times. I knew that if I didn't live right, I probably wouldn't get the opportunity to grow celery, and I wouldn't make thousands of dollars. Then I wouldn't get a Studebaker and I would end up being the same old dud as a senior, as I was now. Then Bobby Jackson wouldn't be the only one who thought I was a twerp, Lydia would too. But I would soon find out that Bobby Jackson was the least of my worries on the path to my dreams.

3. To become a priest I had to be a partner with God.

I didn't hear from Stewart all week. I wondered if he had forgotten all about what I had told him. Each day Delmar would ask what Stewart had said. And each day, I had no answer.

I decided to get up on time for church that Sunday. I wanted to be at Church so I could see Stewart and ask him about the farmers. Mom was surprised when I got up and put on my navy blue suit. I was ready for church a half-hour before it was time to go. As I was impatiently waiting on the sofa, she grinned at me and said, "You look so good in your suit George. I'm glad that you're a priest now—you're a good priest. I love to hear you bless the sacrament."

I liked it when I pleased my mother. She was the best mother in the world. I felt badly that she thought I was a good priest when I didn't feel like I was. But I wanted to be a real priest. I wanted to keep the promise I made just before I was ordained.

I liked church. It's just that I wasn't sure I wanted to be religious. My older brother, Kent, was my hero. But when he was sixteen and I was thirteen, he seemed to stop caring about religion. So I thought I ought to do the same. It was hard having an older brother who was the bishop, and another brother who drank beer, smoked and didn't go to church. I didn't know what direction I wanted to go. All I knew is that I wanted a car so I would be popular with the girls and a "big wheel" at school. Of course my mother wanted me to be religious. She wanted me to go on a mission when I got older. I wasn't sure that I wanted to do that. But that day I was ready to head out for church so that I could see my brother—my bishop.

Before we left that morning my mother cooked me a large breakfast of eggs, bacon, and toast. She always treated me better when she knew I was doing the right things.

When I got to church I wanted to talk to Stewart, but so did everybody else. It was hard to get even a few moments with him. I planned on skipping my Sunday school class so I could talk to him. Usually I hated Sunday school, but this time Brother Young was talking about the Savior. He told us how Jesus drove the money changers out of the temple. He said that Jesus must have really been strong. I was impressed. I wondered if there really was a man named Jesus or if it was just a fairy tale. Some of my friends said they didn't believe all the religious stuff. I didn't know what to believe; but that day in my mind, I could almost see Jesus chasing the money changers. Before I knew it Sunday School was over and I had no time to skip.

In the hallway I saw Stewart. He came toward me and said, "Hey, I've got some good news for you. I've talked to the Storrs brothers and they want to meet you and Delmar on Monday night at seven to talk about your idea of growing celery on their land." Man! I had never heard such good news.

On Monday night Delmar borrowed his Dad's old Plymouth car, and we headed south of town to see the Storrs brothers—George and Alton.

We got lost on our way down, and arrived a half an hour late. We knocked and were greeted at the door by a big round man with a scowl on his face. Rather than greeting us, he simply said, "It's seven thirty! You were supposed to be here at seven. You're a half-hour late." He beckoned us inside. We followed him and sat down. Out of the kitchen came a tall skinny man. He introduced himself, “I’m Alton and you already met my brother, George.”

When we were all seated, there was fear in my heart. The brothers just sat there and stared at us like we were on trial for murder. Finally Alton spoke, “What do you two young fellers have in mind?”

Usually I would have waited for Delmar to answer, but this time I spoke right up. “We want to grow some celery.”

Alton raised his eyebrows and said in a very unfriendly tone, “How could we ever trust two young fellows who don’t even show up on time? How do we know that the celery won’t all dry up waiting for you two to get around to watering it?”

I didn’t know what to say, so I finally replied, “We won’t do that again. That’s a promise.”

“Well, you had better not,” Alton said. “Growing celery means you'll have to get down here real early and you'll have to work until the sun goes down. Celery is the hardest crop there is to grow.”

George looked at me and asked, “Are you guys strong? You have to be strong to grow celery. You’ll have to carry a sprayer on your back, and when its time to harvest you’ll have to lift big crates high over your head to put them on the truck.”

“Delmar is the strongest kid in our school,” I said with excitement.

“What about you?”

"I'll get strong. I'm willing to work hard."

"Can we trust you? We'll be spending a lot of money for celery plants. We don't want you to plant them and then let them die while you sit up at the top of the field drinking water from the well."

"We won't do that. We'll work." I promised.

"Can you work with a horse so you can cultivate and that kind of stuff?" Alton asked.

Delmar spoke up and said, "I worked a lot with horses up in Kamas before my family moved down here."

There was silence and once again they stared at us like we were on trial. Several seconds went by with no one speaking. Finally Alton said, "You guys step outside. George and I need to talk. Don't go anywhere. We'll call you back in a few minutes."

We stood out on the porch for what seemed like an hour. I had never felt so torn up inside. I sure did wish we hadn't been so late. And I sure did wish that I was stronger like Delmar. I was hoping they would agree to our plan but I suspected they might say no. I never wanted anything so much as to have them say yes. I even said a quick prayer in my head.

The door finally opened and they asked us to come back inside. Again, we all sat down. Alton looked at us like we were just fresh out of prison.

George asked, "Why do you want to grow celery? Why not potatoes? They don't take near as much work. How about sugar beets? They're hard, but not as hard as celery."

I looked down in disappointment. I knew we couldn't make enough money in potatoes and beets to buy an old car, let alone a Studebaker. I wasn't going to give up this easily.

I looked up again and said firmly. 'Mr. Storrs and Mr. Storrs, we want to grow celery. If we can't do it for *you*, we'll find someone we *can* do it for."

The brothers looked at each other with surprised looks on their faces. Then George said, "Sounds liked you guys mean business."

"We do." I exclaimed. Delmar looked at me, a little surprised that I had spoken up. I was surprised too! I had never done anything like that before.

Alton said, "Okay, this is the deal, we'll plow a piece of land on the south end of our farm. We haven't plowed it before because it's pasture land. But we think it will be good for celery. There's a flowing well there which is good because it takes a lot of water to grow celery. We'll buy the celery plants. We'll also buy the fertilizer and the bug spray. Bugs like celery, and if you don't spray regularly they'll eat all your plants. In the fall, we'll let you use our truck to take the celery to the packing plant. You boys will have to plant all of the celery. You'll be expected to water, use the horse to cultivate the rows, hoe, and spray for bugs. Then you'll do it all over again. You'll work harder than you have ever worked. And then, in the fall, we'll take the money we've made and split it right down the middle – 50/50. How does that sound?"

I was so choked up with emotion that I could hardly talk. But I muttered, "We'll grow the best celery in the whole county!"

Delmar and I didn't talk all the way up to town. We drove to Don's sweet shop. As we walked in, Delmar didn't look any different, but I knew I looked different. I seemed to be taller. The three girls working behind the counter kept looking at me. They could tell that I looked different too.

When I got home it was time to go to bed. I didn't say anything to Mom and Dad about the celery. But I told dad something I hadn't ever said before. I told him "Good Night." and that I sure did love him. He didn't know how to take that. Then I kissed my mother like I did every night. I told her that I loved her, but that wasn't anything new.

I had a little bedroom at the back of the house. After I got ready for bed, I laid there looking up at the slanted ceiling. I started talking to God in my mind. I did that a lot. I didn't say anything out loud and I didn't kneel down. I just looked up, toward where I figured He was, and I talked to Him in my mind. I knew He could hear me because I could always tell when someone was listening to me. I felt really good whenever I talked to Him like that. I told Him how happy I was about the celery deal. I asked Him to help things work out so I could get the new car. I didn't say Studebaker because I wasn't sure He knew what that was. He seemed to understand, but He didn't make any promise to me about that. At least I didn't hear Him say anything.

I got to thinking about how nice it was to know that there really was a God. I looked forward to Sunday so I could bless the Sacrament to kind of pay Him back.

4. To become a priest I had to be enthused.

It was now mid-April. It had been two weeks since our meeting with the Storrs brothers. After school, I borrowed dad's old 1940 International pick-up truck. I drove down to the place where our celery would make me rich. It was still a big weedy patch of nothing; but in my mind, in my imagination I could see a Studebaker parked right out in the middle of it. I squinted my eyes and saw Lydia sitting in the front seat.

The flowing well was gushing out crystal clear water. Years ago the Storrs family had drilled a 3 inch pipe down into the soil until it hit the ground water. The water had gushed up and never stopped. I loved to watch it and listen to it. It sounded like a mountain stream, and that sound was my favorite sound in the whole world.

Suddenly, I heard a noise behind me and looked up to see a green John Deere tractor coming my way. I soon recognized the driver. It was the big round Storrs brother. He pulled right beside me and turned off the motor. "Let's see," he said, "Its Delmar isn't it?"

"No, I'm George."

"Oh yeah, Delmar is the one who plays football for the Cavemen right? I used to play for the Cavemen. I played high school ball with Hap Holmstead. I had to make big holes in the line and he would run through them. Everyone would cheer for him, and ignore all that I had done. Is Hap your teacher?"

Before I could answer he added, "I just came down to start plowing your field. Are you guys getting ready to plant?"

"Yes sir. We are ready to start as soon as possible."

"Well, I'll plow it today. Tomorrow I'll disk it. Then I'll harrow it and make the rows, and then she'll be ready for you guys to break your back planting her!" With that, he roared with laughter and got to work on his John Deere.

I could hardly keep from shouting! I was so filled with excitement standing there , only days away from my dream. He passed by me to get to the field and I shouted, "Don't run into the Studebaker out there." I knew he couldn't hear me, but I felt like saying it, and so I did.

I stayed as long as I could, and then I had to head home to gather the eggs. Just because I would be rich soon was no reason I could quit gathering eggs. That night, I walked across the street and told Delmar the news. He smiled wider than when he had made the winning touchdown against the Lehi Pioneers.

The next day after school, we both drove down to the field in his dad's Plymouth. We hurried out of the car and stood side by side looking at the field. I had never laid eyes on anything so beautiful. It appeared ten times bigger now. It was smooth and looked like a mile wide tennis court. The soil was darker than black. Delmar and I just stood there in awe. We walked over and I reached down and grabbed a handful of the soil and let it sprinkle back to the ground. I could tell that there was power in that rich soil. I knew it could turn me into the most popular guy to ever walk the halls of dear old American Fork High.

Delmar said, "I've seen a lot of soil in my time, but I've never seen any soil as rich as this. It's even richer than the black soil of Summit County." I knew he knew about soil, and my confidence in our project rose. The soil seemed to be a foundation to the dearest dream that I had ever had. I wanted to say to Delmar, "Let's pray and ask Heavenly Father to bless this field and the soil so that it will grow the best darn celery that has ever been grown." But I didn't say that. I was always afraid to tell Delmar and my other friends how I felt about praying. I didn't want them to think I was trying to be a big religious guy or anything like that. We walked clear around the field. We stayed on the edge because we didn't want to step on the soil and crush it down. We walked and walked because it was a long way around that field. I smiled all the way. It could have been a Guinness record for the longest time a guy ever smiled.

Little did I know that that smile would soon become a frown.

5. To become a priest I had to base my dream on the truth.

We didn't want to go home, but it was time to gather the eggs. We went over to the flowing well, put our faces into the water and had a long drink. I knew that same water would bring life to my dream. Then we headed home.

The next day was Saturday and Stewart came to see Dad and Mom. He came up to our place a lot, and Mom would usually give him something to eat. He was such a good son. Mom was so proud that her son was the bishop. She loved to go to church, and it made her happy that her son was the leader of the ward. My dad didn't go to church because he said that his suit itched. He also said that he took his dog Jake to church once and they told him the dog couldn't come inside. He told them that if the church was too good for the dog, then it was too good for him. But I think he was proud that his son was the bishop. And I was prouder of Stewart being the bishop than I had ever been about anything. I knew I would never be anything like that. I wasn't even sure that I wanted to keep going to church after high school. I thought again of my older brother Kent. He didn't go to church and it didn't seem to hurt him that much. On the other hand, I wondered if being a priest had meant as much to Kent as it was coming to mean to me.

I told Stewart that we had made a deal with the Storrs brothers to be share croppers. He was glad about that. I told him, "They have the field all plowed and ready for planting. So I was wondering when we can start planting them."

"If you plant them too early, there's a chance a frost will come along and damage the tender plants."

I quickly responded, "I don't think it will freeze Stewart. The weather is real warm and I doubt it will get cold again."

"Well, almost every year we get frost in May. You had better wait until after Memorial Day."

"We don't want to wait. If we get it planted now we can harvest it early and that's when the price will be the best. We want to do it next week." I didn't want to back down on this.

"Well, you can do what you want if it's okay with the Storrs brothers. They're the ones who will have to pay for the plants. Talk to them and see what they want to do."

I told Delmar about my talk with Stewart. He said, "We had better wait and do what Stewart says. He knows more about celery than anyone else in town. He's the manager of the Celery Cooperative."

"I know he's smart, but I think he's wrong this time. Do you feel how warm it is right now? It isn't going to freeze any more. I think we should start to plant next week. At least we could plant five or six rows. That way we'll be first to the market and we'll make a lot more money."

The next day we drove down to the Storrs place and talked to Alton and George. We told them that we were anxious to get going and that we needed the celery plants by the next week. They said they would talk to Stewart and find out if it was the right time to plant. I interrupted and told them that I had already talked to Stewart.

"What did he say about the frost?" George questioned.

"He said it was pretty warm and that the chance of a frost wasn't very good."

"Well if he said that, we'll get you some plants next week and you can start putting them in the ground."

That Friday, school let out for the year. As I left my English class and walked down the hall past the auditorium, I saw Lydia. She was coming from the opposite direction. In my mind, I already had my new car. My confidence began bursting over. I walked really close to her so our shoulders brushed up against each other. She was wearing a white Cashmere sweater and a navy blue skirt. Her hair was shimmering as if she had just washed it in Halo Shampoo. There weren't words to describe her beauty. It was like trying to describe a Studebaker. My heart started to pound faster than it had in junior varsity basketball games. But somehow, I wasn't nervous. I felt something inside that I had never felt. I felt like I should turn around, put my arm around her, and walk down the hall just like I had dreamed of doing since I was a sophomore. I nearly did that. But I didn't. Instead, I looked back at her as she walked away. Then she turned around, looked back at me, and said, "I'll see you next year, George."

I smiled and shouted, "I hope I see you before that." She looked at me longingly for what seemed like an hour, and then she was gone.

As I walked down the front steps of American Fork High School, I spoke quietly to myself, "Next year will be my year. I'll have my new car. I'll have the best clothes that Devey's men store has to offer. I'll be on every girl's mind and in their hearts. But it won't do them any good because I'll be the property of Lydia." I had been happy before, but never this happy. It was truly my best day.

But would it be my best summer?

6. *To become a priest I had to listen to my heart.*

On Sunday I was up an hour before it was time to go to church. My mother asked, "What has gotten into you? Why are you up so early?"

"I got up because I was tired of dreaming things while I was asleep. I like to dream things while I'm awake."

Mom laughed, "What are you talking about George?"

"I'm going to grow celery. I'm going to grow celery like Gib Bachelor did. I'm going to make lots of money like he made. I'm going to have a new car—a Studebaker! Have you seen a Studebaker, Mom? It's a dream car. When I get it, I'll take you to church in it. I'm going to be rich,."

"You don't have any land."

"Delmar and I have talked to the Storrs brothers. They are letting us use their land. It will all work out Mom, you just wait and see. You just wait. You'll be so proud of me. "

Just then, Dad came in from feeding the chickens their morning wheat.

"George is going to be rich!" Mom told him with a grin.

“How is he going to do that?”

“He’s going to grow celery.”

She told him about the Storrs brothers. He looked at me like he had never looked at me before. I could see a bit of pride in his eyes. I was never sure he was as proud of me as he was of Stewart and Kent. I think that he thought I was a little bit lazy and that I never cared about anything important. But he could see from the look on my face that I cared about this.

I felt like kidding around with him. I had never done that before. I said, “Get ready Dad and we’ll go to church together.”

He looked at me and said, "My suit itches."

I laughed the way that you laugh when someone you love says something funny. I walked over closer to him and looked into his eyes and said, “I’ve heard that before and I don’t believe it. Get your suit on and let's go. We’ll even take Jake the dog." He frowned at me and then sat down and started to read the newspaper; I could tell that our conversation was over.

Mom was shocked that I had talked to him that way, but I could tell that it pleased her. I gave her a kiss on the cheek. Then I backed off and asked her how I looked in my navy blue suit. Tears came to her eyes and I could tell that I must have looked good. I smiled and announced, “Well, I’m off to church. I have to get there early to help Herbie Pawlowski get things ready for the sacrament.” I sure was feeling good.

BECOMING A PRIESTHOOD MAN

I was soon passing through the mill lane and my mind starting dreaming again. It seemed like every free moment I was seeing that dark, fertile field in my mind. I saw celery growing. I saw trains packed with our celery. I saw a big check being handed to me by Stewart. I saw myself heading to Dave Greenwoods car dealership to pick up my 1948 Studebaker. I saw Lydia and me riding in the car down to the "Owl Inn" to get a cheeseburger.

Fifteen minutes later I arrived at the chapel and my fantasies came to a halt. At the front door I was greeted by Herbie. He informed me that we needed to get the silver trays out of the closet and put the tiny glasses in the holes. Then I needed to go to the sink and fill a pitcher with water to carefully pour in the glasses. When I was finished with that, Herbie asked me to help him put the white linen cloth on the top of the sacrament table. As I helped him get the cloth completely straight, I told him that I sure did like being his friend. It was a different kind of feeling to think about being a priest and doing something this important than it was to think about celery and cars and Lydia. But I still couldn't help thinking about those things first, and my duties as priest second.

As soon as we put the white cloth on top of the trays, I knew we were finished. My mind felt free to wander. The thoughts I had been thinking about the sacrament became surrounded by thoughts of folks having celery cream soup with the celery that I had grown. .

These kinds of thoughts made me feel important. Deep down in my heart, I hadn't felt important for a long time. Oh, I was glad I was a priest in the Aaronic Priesthood. My brother, my bishop, told me that the holding the Priesthood was more important than any other honor. I knew he was right. At least I knew that he thought he was right, but I still didn't really feel it was as important as being a great athlete or being popular at school.

Herbie and I were sitting behind the sacrament table when the chapel began to fill up with people. Mom came in and took her seat on the second row. She looked up at me. I smiled and said a silent hello. She sure did look proud! I liked making her feel proud. Others looked at me. My navy blue suit seemed to make people look at me more than they had in the past.

I usually didn't sing the hymns. But today I just felt like singing. I liked to sing, "Come, Come Ye Saints" and that's what we were singing. I sang so much that I ran out of breath.

Finally, it was time for me to ask Heavenly Father to bless the bread. I knelt down and read the card, "Oh God, the Eternal Father, we ask thee in the name of thy son Jesus Christ…" When I read that I got choked up. I could hardly go on. Herbie was nervous because he didn't know why I'd paused. He whispered the next words to me, but I still couldn't speak. I didn't want people to think I wasn't tough, so I gathered myself together and continued. When I finished, I handed trays of bread to the deacons. When I sat down, I felt exhausted. My hands were trembling a little bit. But I also felt really good and it didn't have any thing to do with celery.

As I sat there waiting for the deacons to return from passing the sacrament, I wondered what was happening to me. I wondered about God and Jesus. I wondered if I should start being a better person; if I should stop acting goofy and acting like I didn't care about religion. I wondered if I should be a man of God like Mom said that Stewart was.

The deacons came back and Herbie said the prayer on the water. Then they left the table to pass it. While they were serving the congregation, I started to think about celery again. In my mind, I could see our whole field filled with the greenest celery ever seen. I liked to eat celery with cheese in the valley part of the stalk. But I wasn't going to eat any of my celery. I needed it all to sell so I could be the richest kid American Fork had ever known.

Little did I know that good feelings could be put out as quick as a candle when the wind hits it.

7. To become a priest I couldn't be a quitter.

Monday morning I was up with the sun. I had not been out of bed so early in the morning since the previous summer when Dad, Mouse Conder, and I had gotten up early to go to the head of American Fork Canyon and climb up to Pittsburg Lake to fish. I had been excited that morning, but not as excited as I was now.

By eight o'clock, Delmar and I were down at the field. I felt as though I was in the dressing room waiting to play a big game. George Storrs had made furrows for twelve rows of celery. He had the plants on his old Chevrolet pick up truck. He said, "There they are. I'm glad it's you guys planting them and not me."

We walked over to the little wooden boxes that held the plants. There were about fifty in a box. I picked one up and looked at it. I couldn't believe what I was holding in my hands. I smelled it. It smelled like celery all right! I grinned and glanced over at Delmar. He didn't look nearly as excited as I felt. Delmar never did feel as deeply about all this as I did. He didn't dream like I dreamed, at least I didn't think he did. But then I realized that dreams were kind of personal. Maybe he dreamed of different things.

Inside I said silently, "Heavenly Father bless these little plants and help each one to grow into celery the size of a tree." I was just kidding about that and the Lord knew it. I just wanted Him to know how deeply I felt about all of this.

We opened the dam that was preventing water from reaching our rows. The water level slowly rose until some of it began to trickle into the head of the first two furrows. Soon the water was seeping from the stream in the furrow into the soil along each bank. It was making that part dark and muddy.

Stewart drove up in his blue truck. It always felt good to see him, but this time it was like the coming of the Lord. He came over and Mr. Storrs said, “Stewart will tell you boys how to do this. He knows all there is to know about celery.”

“All right,” Stewart said as he picked up a plant, “First we cut an inch off the bottom of the two inch root. If we don't cut it off and we plant it so it isn’t straight down, the root will curl up. Then as the plant begins to grow, the root will have to turn around and head down and that will set the celery back two weeks. You have to get the roots straight down.” It seemed to me that Stewart was the smartest man in the world.

As we watched, Stewart planted the first plant. He then stood back as we all looked at the little plant in the big field. It looked lonely there. But I knew that big things had to start as little things. He chuckled with satisfaction and said, “Well, there you go. Now you can start. After you have planted fifty-thousand plants six inches apart you’ll be finished.”

“Fifty thousand,” I thought. “Man! It will take all summer just to plant them.”

Delmar chose a row and I walked over to a different one. I bent over and planted my first celery plant. I put my finger right along side the celery plant with the tip of the root at the tip of my finger. I pushed it down into the mud and pulled my finger out. The water and the mud came into where my finger had been and the plant was planted. I was successful. It looked like the best little celery plant in the history of farming. I could almost see a five dollar bill curled up in the leaves of it.

BECOMING A PRIESTHOOD MAN

It sure was fun planting those first fifty celery plants. But it took longer than I had thought it would. It was a hot day for May. My back got a kink in it. I could see the end of the row as I looked south. But it was ten miles away. I thought of going to the flowing well and getting a drink. Instead, I kept on planting. I knew that making dreams come true required lots of work, sweat, and sometimes pain. So I kept planting--take a little plant, line it up on my finger, press my finger and the plant down into the mud, pull my finger out, and press the mud against the plant.

It would be simple to do that one time or even twenty times, but to do it a hundred and then a thousand times while being bent over like I was in a Chinese torture chamber was more than I could bear to think about. I realized why I had always been lazy in the past. Being lazy wasn't bad compared to this kind of work. I could see Delmar was faster than I was, and now he was about three yards ahead of me. It was probably easier for him because he wasn't as tall as I was and the ground was closer to him. I knew I should hurry, but I wanted to do it right. Each plant would put five dollars in my pocket, so they had to be planted with the root straight down.

I kept at it though sheer willpower. Just the way Hap Holmstead said the POWs stayed alive until the war ended. The end of the row seemed a little closer, but not much. When I reached it I would be able to straighten up and get a cold drink out of the flowing well. I knew I had to think about something other than planting celery or the pain and suffering would get to me. I needed to think of something pleasant.

I decided to think about Lydia and how friendly she was the last time I saw her. It seemed like she was trying to tell me that she liked me. I should have gone over and said to her,

"What's up Lydia? I can see you have something on your mind. You can tell me. You can trust me with your deepest thoughts or concerns. What is it Lydia?" Then I knew she would have said, "George, you sure are sensitive. You always think of others before you think of yourself. That is why everyone admires you so much"

Then she would laugh in the way that only she could laugh. Her eyes would sparkle, and her white teeth glisten as she said, "You look like a rich kid who just moved to Utah from California."

My dreaming was interrupted when I heard Delmar ask, "How's it going? Kind of hard isn't it?"

I could now see that Delmar was further down the row. I was sure that he was thinking about celery plants and not girls. I was sure that no girl had ever told him that he looked like a guy from California. But I didn't tell him that. Instead I decided I had better be more like him and concentrate on the celery.

Finally, after what seemed like two hours, Delmar was at the end of the row and was working his way back on my row. Then we met. He had a watch. "What time is it?" I asked.

"Nine," he replied.

"Nine! Man I thought it would be at least ten."

We walked up to the top of the field to get a drink of water. I looked at every celery plant that we passed. They looked like they were already starting to grow. I wondered how much each of them would bring on the market place in New

York City. Maybe, because we planted them earlier than any one else would plant theirs, they would be worth more than five dollars a plant. I felt happy. It felt good not to be planting celery. It was easier to think of the dream than it was to make the dream come true.

The water tasted better than a tall cold glass of Hires Root Beer. It was the best drink I think I have ever had.

Delmar headed back to the third row. I thought, "Let's rest a little," but I didn't say that. I followed him and got a bunch of celery plants and went to work. My back felt a little better. I was getting used to being bent over. But a few minutes later, I felt a sharp pain in the lower part of my back. Delmar never looked up, but I stood and stretched. He kept on planting. I decided to get back to it. I started to think about my new car to ease the pain of bending over.

My mind wandered to the previous Wednesday night. I had been at Owl Inn when Lloyd Wright drove up in his father's new car. I asked him where he got it. He told me from the Chevrolet Dealership.

I asked, "Do they sell Studebakers there?"

He said that there wasn't any place in American Fork to buy a Studebaker. He added, "You have to go to Provo to get one of those. Dave Greenwood can get one. He gets all kind of cars at his car lot." Then he looked at me like he was really curious and asked, "Why do you care about Studebakers?"

I didn't answer. But someday he would find out.

My mind then came back to the celery. Delmar was ahead of me again and I knew I had better think less and work more if I was going to keep up with him.

But I couldn't quit thinking. I wondered what Dave Greenwood would think when I walked in next fall and asked him if he could get me a new Studebaker Commander. I could see the look on his face as he asked, "Why would a young guy like you want to talk about a Studebaker? Shouldn't you be over at Gambles Store asking about the price of a bike?" Then I would tell him that I could pay cash.

I knew that he would tell all the people he knew about the Durrant kid having a boat-load of money. The news would soon be all over town. Lydia's dad would hear about it and ask her at the dinner table how come I was so rich. She would be impressed and would want to know more. She would probably go to Thornton Drug each night in her nice coat, hoping I would walk in and say, "Hey Lydia, would you like me to buy you a cherry iron port? I've got plenty of cash you know." She would swoon and almost fall down. It would start her to thinking about how much fun it would be to go with me to the Homecoming Dance.

By now, I had planted about twenty plants without even thinking about it. I looked back and they seemed to be planted right. Delmar was now twice as far down the row as I was. I tried to hurry, but it was hard. It was hard enough to go slow let alone speed up. I kind of wished that Delmar wasn't there so I could work at my own pace and not his. But we were partners and so I knew I had to try harder to keep up.

It went on like that all morning. It was hot! I missed my old job as a garbage collector. That's what I had done last summer. I had been a garbage collector for the city of American Fork. It had paid really well. Just this other old guy and I collected all the garbage in American Fork. We had a big truck. We had to lift the old metal garbage cans up and empty them out over the top rack of the truck. Sometimes some of the garbage, like peach skins and pits, and rotten tomatoes would fall back in my face. But even that wasn't as bad as having my back aching like it had been hit by a German torpedo.

The only thing about collecting garbage that made it a bad job was that people saw me doing it. It hadn't done much to make people think I was popular guy. I had nightmares that Lydia would see me. Man that would have been the worst thing that could ever have happened. I would've hated to have her see me with garbage dripping off my chin. She would've turned away and thought, "How could someone as wonderful and handsome as George be a garbage collector?"

We finally got the two rows done. Then it was time for lunch.

"How is your back?" Delmar asked.

"Good," I replied.

Delmar said, "My back feels like it did when the Lehi football players kept tackling me on a drive to score the winning touchdown. I thought I would never be able to walk again after that game."

"Mine hurts a little," I replied.

"You're doing good," he said.

I didn't answer, but it sure did make me happy to get a compliment like that from next year's All-State fullback and the guy who was popular with girls as far away as Lehi, Utah.

It took another day and a half to get those first twelve rows planted. I was never so glad to see something end. It reminded me of how I had felt when I was a kid waiting for the last day of school to be over so I could start having some fun.

Stewart told us we should wait a couple of weeks before we planted any more. He said that he didn't want to see our whole crop wiped out if the weather turned cold and a frost came into the valley. I was glad he said that, but at the same time I thought, "Yes, we would be risking it. But if we prayed, it would be all right; and if we got to the market earlier, we would make even more money than Gib Bachelor made last year."

But a two-week planting break seemed good too. There wasn't too much work to do on our celery crop those two weeks. The plants were too young to cultivate or to hoe. They didn't need fertilizer yet. So we'd just go down in the morning and use a ruler to see how much the celery had grown. It grew about a hundredth of an inch the first week. I couldn't see the marks on my ruler very well, but I could tell it was about a hundredth of an inch. I knew I was a hundredth of an inch closer to my new car and popularity and then...

In the middle of the second week, I could see clouds gathering. Pretty soon there was a fierce wind. I was out gathering eggs, and as I headed back to the cellar I could feel the air suddenly turn cold.

That night, after Dad listened to the news on KSL radio, he told my mom, "The man on the radio said that it might freeze tonight."

"Oh no," Mother replied in a painful voice. “Do you think it will kill our apricots again like it did last year?"

I didn’t hear his reply. I didn’t care about apricots. All I cared about was celery. I headed to my bedroom to do some serious praying. I couldn’t bear to lose all of that celery that I had worked so hard to plant.

“Please dear God, you know I’m doing real good at church. Don’t let it freeze my celery.” I hoped Delmar was praying too, but I wasn’t sure that he was because he and my friends didn’t feel about prayer the way that I did. At least I didn’t think they did. I never asked them about it.

At breakfast Mom told me, “I’m so sad it got our apricots. We won’t have any jam or jelly this year.”

I didn’t dare ask her about celery.

Delmar and I drove down to the bottoms with fear in our hearts. Would our green celery plants be black from a death by freezing?

I kept peering out of the window as Delmar drove closer and closer to our field. The celery looked nice and green at a distance. When we got close, I shouted out, "It didn't get it. It looks as good as it did yesterday. It’s okay Delmar! It’s okay!" I couldn’t tell if he was as happy as I was, because he didn’t show his emotions the way I did. I was sure the celery was all right.

Sure enough the celery was all right.

Pretty soon, I could see Stewart's blue truck coming to our field. I ran to meet him shouting, "The frost didn't hurt our celery Stewart. We'll still be rich."

He got out and walked silently past me, and went to the first row. He walked down several feet and knelt down by a plant. I wondered, "Why did he have to do that? He could tell just by looking at it that it was all right."

He pushed the stems aside and looked down right into the middle of the plant. Then he went to the next one, and the next. What was he doing? Couldn't he see the plants hadn't been hurt?

"Come and look," he said.

Delmar and I hurried over. "Look right here. See this? This little part of the plant is the heart. See that black part? That plant has frozen. And those others have too. I'm sorry to tell you this, but all twelve rows are ruined."

"They don't *look* ruined." I argued. "You're wrong Stewart. Look at the leaves. They're green just like they were yesterday."

"Well, I've seen it before. It isn't the leaves that are dead; it's the heart that's destroyed. These plants will grow, but when they're bigger they'll go to seed. They will never be normal celery plants. You'll never be able to sell them."

After several seconds of silence, Stewart spoke again. "I'm sorry to tell you this. I know how hard you've worked.

But you’ll be just as well to have Mr. Storrs plow them under and you can start over.”

I spoke out in pure pain, “We aren’t starting over! I can tell they’re not hurt!”

“Well, you’ll have to decide. But I’m telling you you’ll never sell any celery from those plants."

Delmar just stood there. He didn’t argue. He just took it. I wasn’t going to take it. Stewart knew about things, but he didn’t know everything.

“What about other people's celery? Is it hurt too?” Delmar asked.

“Other people didn’t plant early like you guys did. You could have had a real advantage on them, but it was a risk. Farming is a risk. You’d just as well go to Las Vegas and gamble as to be a farmer. You guys took a risk and you lost. I’m real sorry, boys. But I’m proud that you tried. Now you just get back to work. That was the last frost. What you do from here on out won’t freeze.”

“To heck with it," I said. "I’m not going to start over. It isn't worth it. We’ll just have bad luck again.”

Stewart put his hand on my shoulder and said, “Quit talking like that. No dream ever came true for a quitter. You’ve got to stay with it. I’ll have the Storrs brothers get you some more plants and you can start again tomorrow. Things will work out if you’re willing to work.”

At lunch that day, Mom was complaining about losing her apricots to the frost. I didn't say anything, but it seemed like she should have cared more about my celery and less about her apricots. She had lost a few jars of jelly. I had lost my new car and my senior year. Now I would be as big a dud as I had been my junior year. Besides, I had seen Lydia going into a movie with a guy from Lehi the night before. I wished the police would arrest guys from Lehi who came over to American Fork to take our girls. Taking girls was worse than being a cattle rustler in my mind. I felt really discouraged. "Why is life so hard? Why don't dreams come true?" I wondered. I didn't pray that night.

The next morning, I felt like sleeping in. But I could smell that Mom had made pancakes and so I got up. When we got back down to our field, Delmar got right out of the car. I didn't want to get out. I wanted to just sit there. After about three seconds, I didn't know what to do and so I slowly got out. There were six boxes of celery plants. The Storrs brothers had not only brought the plants, but they had brought the tractor and had harrowed the twelve rows right out of the ground. I almost died when I saw that. They didn't have a right to do that. They had also made new rows where we could re-plant. It was easy for them to plow our rows. It only took them a half hour. They hadn't planted them one by one. They hadn't nearly broken their backs leaning over for days. I decided that they weren't being fair to us. We had to do all the work and they got half of our money.

Delmar took his shovel, pulled out the head gate, and pretty soon the water was starting down the rows. "Let's go," he said. "We have a lot of work to do."

I felt like saying, “You do it. You’re the big football star." But I knew we were partners and so I got a bundle of plants, cut off the roots, and walked to the head of my row.

I don’t think I’ve ever done anything as hard as planting that first plant. It wasn’t the work of pushing the plant in. It was the idea of doing something over that I had already done once. The next plant went in, and the next. My mind started to change. I started to feel a little of my dream coming back. I could hear Stewart saying, “Things will work out if you’ll go to work.” It seemed like Stewart was the wisest man in the whole town.

Somehow, I was getting faster at planting. I was keeping up with Delmar. I decided to see if I could pass him up. But he saw what I was doing and went faster. I smiled. I hadn’t done that in two days. I asked him, “How will we do in football this year?”

“Depends on how well Mark Grant does at quarterback. You’ve got to have a good quarterback to win.”

“You can run every time; you don’t need any passing.”

He didn’t answer. I wished I played football, but I was more of a basketball player. Tall and skinny. I hated that I was skinny. I wished that I was a big, broad-shouldered guy like the Lehi guy who had taken Lydia to the movie. I knew that girls liked strong guys. “Of course, a guy with a car is more popular with the girls than a strong guy. I’ll bet that guy from Lehi borrowed the car from his dad. I’ll have my own car, and that guy will be standing on the sidewalk watching me drive away with Lydia.” I thought to myself.

I was almost keeping up with Delmar. I was shocked at how hot the day was. I didn't see how it could freeze at night and then be so hot the next day. But it kind of felt good.

We were about a fourth of the way down the row and it hadn't seemed to take long at all. This wasn't so bad after all.

I got to thinking about how disappointed I had been when Stewart said our celery was ruined. I hated disappointment more than any other thing in life. Disappointment made me just want to sit and not get up. I remembered two years earlier when American Fork lost the championship in basketball to Grantsville. That was the saddest day of my life. My brother Kent was our star. I was so proud to be his brother. His name was in the paper every night. He scored more points in most games than the whole other team. We won every game that year, and I was right there on the front row cheering as loudly as I could. A lot of girls said hello to me because I was Kent's brother. Lydia brought me an article she had cut out of the *Deseret News* about Kent being the best player in Utah for a long time. When she handed it to me, she said, "I know you will be even better than your brother."

When she said that, I was happy and sad. I just didn't think I could ever be as good as my brother. But maybe I could. That night I went out into the barn where we had a basketball standard. I shot long shot after long shot. That was the way Grantsville beat American Fork. Bill Ray Jeffries, their guard, had hit long shot after long shot. He made twenty four points, all on long shots.

I knew that when I was a senior, I would be the one shooting long shot after long shot. I would lead our team to victory. But first I needed a car. Bill Ray Jeffries came to our school dance after he had beaten us in basketball. All the girls in our town were in love with him. He had dark hair and looked like a movie star. I knew if I had a car I would look like a movie star, too. I would look like a guy who had just moved here from California. Then I'd be more confident.

An athlete had to have confidence to make long shots. Without confidence, the shot would always just barley miss. Next year, I would be confident because of my Studebaker. Also, to be good at basketball you had to look like a movie star. The starting five players on a basketball team were usually the five best-looking guys in the school. Nobody had to be handsome to play foot ball. A lot of ugly guys played football and nobody even knew it. The helmet covered them up.

By now we were nearly to the end of the row. Delmar was about twenty feet ahead of me. He finished his row and then helped me with mine. My back didn't hurt like it had before. Delmar was tired. He looked at me in a way that made me think he wished I was a better worker. I could tell that he didn't want to have to help me with my row. We walked to the top of the field. We each had a cold drink of water. I felt happy inside. I knew there were more rows to plant. But I was eager to get at it.

Nothing could stop me now. Or could it?

8. To become a priest I had to grow and mature in many ways.

That night I told my mom, "Mom I'm sure sad about you losing your apricots. I sure will miss that jelly and the jam. You know how to make that kind of stuff better than any other mother in the world." I even helped her clean up the dishes. I had never done that before, but I just felt like helping. She finally sat down, and I went over and sat by her. I was getting bigger, but I still liked to sit by her. She liked that too. I loved her so much. She was always so proud of me even if I was a twerp. She thought I was the best there was in town. I never wanted to do anything to make her sad. That's why I didn't swear and say bad words. At least I tried not to. I didn't want her to be disappointed in me.

Two weeks later our whole field was covered by celery plants. But the plants were so little the field looked more like black soil than green celery. But they were there and they were growing a hundredth of an inch each day. Stewart said that after awhile they would start to spread out and the field would look all green. I could hardly wait for the plants to grow.

Delmar and his family went up to Kamas for a family reunion. So I went down to the field on my own to water the tiny plants. I liked to be down there on my own. When Delmar was there I let him lead out in all the work because he knew so much more than I did about farming. I turned the water on to the first ten rows. An hour later, I moved the water onto the next ten rows. It wasn't hard work and there was a lot of time to think.

While I waited for the rows to get soaked, I took the ruler out of my back pocket where I kept it with my comb. I measured the plant that looked the biggest. I almost jumped for joy. It had grown a fourth of an inch since last week.

Growing was one of my favorite things. I started thinking about my growing. I remembered that when I was in the sixth grade I was the biggest kid in the school except for Frosty Vest. He was a giant. But among the normal kids I was the biggest. Then I stopped growing. I just stayed the same size, month after month, and even year after year. Guys that had been smaller than me became bigger than me. I wanted to grow really bad. But the more that I wanted to grow the more that I stayed the same. My brother was big. I wanted to be big like him, but I was little. I prayed to grow, and I couldn't. People would ask me, "Your brother is big, when are you going to grow?"

I had felt bad that I was little. I started worrying about being little. I started to think that I wasn't good because I wasn't big. When I was a sophomore, some of my friends had strong muscles and one even started to shave. I had wished I was the guy who shaved. Then the girls would've said, "George shaves." Then Lydia wouldn't have even wanted to go out with the Lehi guys. I knew I shouldn't have felt bad about the way that I looked. But I did.

My mind wandered to the end of my junior year. During the last three months of that year, I started to grow. I grew from five foot eight inches to six feet. I was so happy about that. I had dreamed of being six feet. Growing was about the best thing a guy could do if he wanted to be a basketball player; and of course combing his hair so he'd look good on the court. I mean, whoever saw a short basketball player or one that didn't comb his hair?

The rows became soaked and I turned the water off. I heard the rumble of a truck behind me. I looked up the old dirt road and saw that it was Stewart's old blue truck. He pulled over, jumped out, and walked over to me. He told me it was time to do some fertilizing. He didn't mean horse manure. He meant chemical fertilizer. He said a liberal dose of Ammonium Sulfate could start those plants to growing faster than anything I had seen. I was glad that Delmar would be coming home that afternoon so that he would be there to get that started.

The Storrs brothers came the next day and they sure did seem pleased with the way that Delmar and I were working things. George, the big one, told us, "Good work boys." Alton didn't talk but he did smile a little. They unloaded ten bags of ammonium sulfate.

Stewart had told us to open the bag, carry it down the row, and make a line of sulfate right along side the plants. It needed to be right where the water ran. He said the water would dissolve the fertilizer and it would go right to the roots of the plants. Then, the plants would gobble it up and turn it into celery.

Those bags were heavy. They were not a problem for Delmar to carry. He was as strong as an ox. But for me they were heavy. I thought it would be nice to sit and watch as Delmar spread the fertilizer. But he said, "Come on, you can do this." I picked up a bag and started down a row. It got lighter and lighter as the sand-like substance poured out. But then I had to get another bag. After a few bags, just when I thought I couldn't carry even one more, something that I couldn't explain happened. I started to get more strength. Carrying a full bag became easier. I thought to myself, "I'm getting stronger. I like this! This will help me in basketball because you got to be strong to get rebounds and steals." I felt happy I was getting stronger.

I began to kind of enjoy hard work. I had never liked hard work but now, in a way, it felt good. I sure did sleep well after carrying those bags.

It took us two days, but we finally fed all fifty thousand of those little celery plants.

I started to get a few noticeable muscles. My body was changing. I liked to stand in front of the mirror and comb my hair.

On the Fourth of July, my friend, Mouse Conder, came over and we sat out on the front lawn. He told me how he wanted to be a hair dresser when he grew up. He asked me if he could comb my hair for me. I decided to let him have a try. He got it all wet. Then he combed it back. Then he made it like it was little hills, one in front and three more after that. For the first time my hair looked wavy. It never had been wavy before, but Mouse had made it wavy. I looked really good. My brother Kent even said that it looked good. Mouse then taught me how to comb it into a duck tail in the back. The guys who were really popular all had duck tails.

My mom told me on Sunday morning that I really looked handsome, but that my suit pants were too short. She said that the two of us should go to JC Penney and get me a new suit. We went on Wednesday after I got home from the celery field, gathered the eggs, took a hot bath and got my hair all wavy. We chose the navy blue suit. It looked good on me; I could tell that navy blue was my color. I knew I'd sure look good the next week at the sacrament table. I wished that Lydia was in the fourth ward where I went to church. Instead she was in the third ward. I wanted to go to church over there, but I was too much needed in my own ward. I knew that if she could see me in my navy blue suit, with my wavy hair, she would go to pieces.

The celery now covered the whole field like a big green rug. The Ammonia Sulphate really worked. I wondered if I could put some in my oatmeal. I could use three more inches before the basketball season started in November. When I stood up by the flowing well and saw that green field I was the proudest guy in the town. I imagined the celery plants slowing morphing into ten-dollar bills.

We were now hoeing the plants for the second time. Stewart told us that hoeing would loosen the roots so that they could get more air. He also said it would allow the water to come up from deeper down and give the plants a drink. I liked hoeing.

I would sing to Delmar, "Hi Hoe. Hi Hoe." He didn't sing much. I loved working with him anyways. He had moved to American Fork, right next door to me, from Kamas when we started the ninth grade. I had known all the American Fork girls since we were in the first grade. But as soon as he came, the girls got really excited. It was like they had never seen a guy before, and they flocked around him. It made me wish I could have moved into town. Then I would've been popular.

Delmar was big and strong and he had black wavy hair. The first day of gym class, we had all learned that he was an athlete. He ran faster and jumped higher than any of us. The coaches were so happy he had moved in. The first week he was there he'd been elected junior high president. I had always wanted to be elected to something, but had never been nominated.

Delmar could also dance really well. I couldn't dance, and I didn't know how to learn. If I could have danced better I would have been more popular. I went to the dances, but I just stood on the side and watched. People would ask me to dance and I'd say no. I really did want to. But it took confidence to dance to be out there with everybody looking at you.

Because he was right next door to me, he and I became best friends. That made me happy because there were always girls around when I was with him. I just wished more of them had been friendlier to me instead of showering him with all their attention.

Anyway, as we were hoeing we got to talking about horses and climbing Mount Timpanogos and about the American Fork Steelers baseball team and about hamburgers and fries and all sorts of stuff. Then we got to telling each other more about our feelings. He said he thought I would be more popular with the girls if I didn't have such a long nose. That really hurt me. So I said, "Well your nose is too short and spread out so it just doesn't look right."

I could tell it hurt him for me to say that, but he had said something that had hurt me and so I had every right to hurt him. We quit talking after that. But I then knew my nose was too long and he knew his was too short.

I think it bothered me more than him because he had confidence and I didn't. We didn't talk all the rest of the day, but we hoed faster than we had ever hoed. While we were going home I almost told him I was sorry. But I didn't. I think he knew I was sorry. It was just too hard to say, "I'm sorry." It was easier to think it. I thought that he must have thought that he was sorry too. I got out of the car and didn't say anything. He didn't either.

That night I thought that it was sad that two good friends could quit being friends just because their noses were different. I told Heavenly Father I was sorry and hoped that he would tell Delmar that. The next morning he was really friendly and so was I.

My dream was closer than ever to coming true. I couldn't remember a time in my life when I was so happy. That night, when I was brushing my teeth, I looked into the mirror and my nose seemed shorter. I felt like nothing could ever go wrong again.

But…

9. To become a priest I had to do things that I never before thought I could do.

The next day, we saw Stewart coming in his blue truck. He was driving faster than we had ever seen him drive. He bounded from his truck even before it had fully stopped. He almost ran over to us. "I've got some really bad news for you boys. There is an infestation of leaf hoppers in the valley." He added, "Those pests could wipe out your whole field in a day."

Delmar looked as white as a ghost and asked, "What can we do about it?"

"You have got to spray-- starting today."

I was shocked and muttered, "We don't know how to spray."

Stewart could sense our fears and said, "Maybe we can beat this. Maybe there is still time. I would suggest that if you have ever prayed you do it now."

He added, "I stopped by the Storrs house and they will have some spray and a back pack sprayer down here within an hour. The direction on how to mix the insecticide with water is on the jugs of spray. They will show you how to use the sprayer. It will take time so you will have to work tonight until dark and then get up and get down here at daylight tomorrow. I've got to go warn others of the hoppers."

I hadn't seen Stewart so concerned since the fourth ward church house had caught on fire two years earlier.

I walked over by the well while Delmar finished talking to Stewart. I had to be alone. I acted like I was looking at the well, but I was really praying. I was good at acting like I wasn't praying when I was. In a minute Delmar came over. He was really silent. I could tell that he was praying too.

I asked God to stop those insects in their tracks. I knew he could do that because of the control he had over the insects in the plagues of Egypt in the Old Testament. Without God helping, I could see my dream disappearing right before my eyes. All that hard work and now it could soon be gone. Farming sure was a bigger gamble than going to Las Vegas.

I felt worse than during the last minutes of the game against Grantsville when I knew all was lost. In my mind, I could see Lydia walking away from me and into the arms of the guy from Lehi.

I could hear a truck racing its engine. I looked around and saw the Storrs brothers coming as fast as the old truck would take them.

They unloaded the backpack sprayer and ten gallon jugs of spray. They said they had to get back to their other fields to spray their cabbage and onions. Delmar started reading directions and told me to open the first gallon. Pretty soon we had it all mixed up and the backpack tank was full and ready to go. It reminded me of the flame thrower stuff I had seen in the newsreels about the fighting in the South Pacific against the Japanese. But this was more important than that.

Delmar loaded it on his back and fastened the straps. He started to pump the lever with his right hand and arm and then he aimed the spray nozzle down at the ground. The white, foamy substance came out and he ran to the first row and began dousing each plant with spray. It was going to take a long time.

I didn't know how to help except to stand there and pray some more. Pretty soon Delmar came back and told me it was empty. "Let's fill her up again," I said. "I'll mix it up while you rest." He agreed. He was sweating great drops of sweat. I could see that the back of his shirt was drenched in moisture.

He then loaded it on his back and took off faster than he ran in football. Soon he had two rows done. This was going to take a long time. I kept looking for a horde of insects darkening the sky as they came a flying in. But I couldn't see any yet.

When Delmar returned I said, "I'll take the next one."

He replied, "I'm still okay. Let's wait until I'm too tired to keep going and then you can take a turn."

I could sure tell why Delmar was the best foot ball player in the state. He was the strongest guy I had ever seen. Nothing could get him down. That tank must have weighed about ninety pounds.

After two hours Delmar began to look sick. His face was pale and he looked like he was about to throw up. He took a short break but quickly hurried back into the field. He had gone about twenty yards when I saw him stumble and fall. I hurried to where he was and undid the straps. He said he had cramps and was in great pain. I didn't know it then, but his back was drenched in the insecticide.

I helped him up and he put his arm on my shoulder as we walked out of the field. We got to the car and he couldn't even open the door he was so weak. I opened it and sort of pushed him in. I drove as fast as I could up to the old American Fork Hospital. The doctor looked at him and said something has poisoned him. I told him about the spray and he said, "We better get him some medicine. That stuff could kill him." The doctor was able to save Delmar, but he also ordered him to spend a week on bed-rest.

I didn't know what to do. I couldn't spray that whole field. I didn't think I could even carry that heavy tank on my back. But I knew that I had to. Our entire dream was up to me.

Delmar's mother came, and I left the hospital and drove back to the field. As I drove along, my mind was filled with doubt. I said softly to myself, "Maybe it would be best to not have a dream, they never come true anyway." I went down into the field and carried the sprayer back up to the well. I could hardly carry it and it was only half full.

As I got back to the well I saw a leaf hopper jump in front of me. I stomped on it, but it still hopped toward our celery. That hopper seemed to know that there wasn't any food as tasty as celery. The enemy had officially arrived. I had a pair of pliers in my car. I found where the sprayer was leaking and tightened it up. If we had only done that before, Delmar would be all right.

I took the half full machine and tried to throw it on my back the way that Delmar did. It nearly pulled me over backwards. But I finally got it on and started pumping with my right arm. Soon I was back in the field where Delmar had gone down. It was hard to walk on the uneven soil. As I moved forward I stumbled and fell. I put my hands down and was able to push myself back up. I sprayed the first plant and the second. I made it to the end of the row. I was thirsty and sweaty, but I could tell my shirt wasn't getting wet the way that Delmar's had. I knew that I was all right and wouldn't get poisoned. I started up the other row. The tank was empty. I hurried to the top of the field. My mouth seemed to be full of cotton, but I felt that this wasn't the time for me to get a drink.

I mixed the insecticide with the water. Now would be the test. Could I lift the full tank onto my back? I knew that I couldn't. It was just too heavy. I thought about emptying half of it out, but if I did that each time, spraying the whole field would take too long. The Hoppers would've had it all devoured while I fiddled with the next ten rows.

With nervous tension, I filled it all the way up. I felt that I had to. I took a deep breath and thought, "Oh please God help me get it on my back." I used every ounce of strength I could muster and finally it was on. And I was still upright. I cinched up the straps and staggered to the next row. It was hard to cross the ditch at the top of the field; it seemed as large as the Grand Canyon. But I finally made it. I was pumping with my right hand like a mad man. With my left hand I aimed and pulled the lever and the first plant was doused with hopper killer.

I moved to the next plant. I was wishing Lydia could see me doing this. She would have thought it was the greatest thing ever. I smiled a little smile. I didn't have energy to smile a big smile. I was soon half-way down the row. I could do this! I really could do this. I couldn't believe I could do this. Maybe I could do a lot of other hard things.

Little did I know that the hardest part was still on its way.

10. To become a priest I had to get over any things that had held me back in the past.

Like my celery, I was changing, I was growing, but I had so far to go.

I didn't know why I couldn't live the way that I dreamed. In my dreams I could say things to Lydia and act like I was Clark Gable, the movie star. But in real life, if I saw Lydia I froze up. I couldn't get my face to loosen up, and I couldn't get my tongue to say things that made sense. When it would come time for her to leave, and I had not done anything like I had dreamed, I'd feel really bad. The way I acted in real life made me feel like I was like Clark Kent instead of Super Man--like a twerp instead of a hero.

Like when dad and I rode downtown in the old International Truck to get feed for the chickens, and to buy some groceries for Mom.

Dad liked to buy the main groceries at Chipman's Store, but he preferred to buy meat from Bradley's Market. Lydia worked for Tom Bradley because he was her Uncle. I really liked him because he told me every time I came in that the basketball coach should start me instead of Leroy Griffin. I liked that.

On the other hand, I knew as soon as we walked into Bradley's market that I would be face to face with Lydia. That thrilled me, but it also scared me. I couldn't figure out why it scared me. It just did. As we walked in, right there at the main counter was Lydia. I didn't know how to talk, but I sure did know how to feel. My heart started racing, and I knew I was laying eyes on the most beautiful sight ever seen by mankind. She knew how to talk, "Hello George." No one could say George the way that she did—she couldn't have said it that way if she didn't have deep and abiding feelings for me.

I answered, "Hello." I said the word like it should be said, but my eyes didn't make contact with hers. And I felt like backing up instead of charming my way up closer. I started to look up, when, out of the corner of my eye, near the coffee, I spotted Bobby Jackson. I knew I had chosen the worst time to come into Bradleys. I'd sooner see Baby Face Nelson, the world's biggest crook than to see Bobby Jackson.

It had all started when I was in the third grade, and Bobby moved to town. He came from Georgia. He was husky. He didn't seem to have a neck. He looked like a good kid so I wanted to be friendly, and I said, "Hi." He replied, "Who are you talking to? I don't know you." He had said it so loudly that others heard it, and I felt like crawling into a hole. He had always had a way of making me feel like crawling into a hole.

One day I was downtown with my brother Kent. We were sitting in the car, waiting for Dad to come out of the barber shop, and there came Bobby walking down the sidewalk past People's State Bank. My Brother Kent had heard that

Bobby was the toughest third grader in town. He rolled down the window and shouted, “Are you Bobby Jackson?” I slumped way down in my seat. Bobby stopped walking and looked over toward our car. I hoped that he didn’t see me. Then Kent said, “My brother George tells me that he isn’t afraid of you.”

I about died. Why did he say that? Bobby looked closer and he could see me there. He came over to the truck and said, “George, do you want to make something of it?” That is what we used to say when we were offering to go behind the Apollo Dance hall and fight somebody.

I didn’t know what to say. I knew Kent wouldn’t let him beat me up. Kent could’ve easily beaten up Bobby. Kent was the toughest kid in the town. He just wanted to make me feel bad; he kind of liked to do that.

Bobby added, “Any time you want, we can see who is afraid of who.”

I timidly defended myself, “I didn’t say what Kent said I said.”

“Well you had better never say it or I'll beat you up as much as Max Schmeling got beat up in his last fight with Joe Louis.”

I didn’t say any more and Bobby went on his way.

I felt like the biggest coward in the town. Kent didn’t know how I felt. He didn’t seem to care.

Ever since then, whenever I saw Bobby Jackson I felt really small in my heart. He had never hit me or pushed me.

But he said things that made me feel little. People used to say, “Sticks and stones may break my bones but names will never hurt me.” That statement just wasn’t true. I sometimes wished that he would beat me up and then leave me alone. That would hurt, but not as badly as feeling that I wasn’t a real person.

I tried to never be where Bobby Jackson was, but every once in awhile I couldn’t avoid it. And every time he said something that took away my confidence.

Now there he was in Bradley's Market. I hoped that he wasn’t there to see Lydia. He wasn’t good enough for Lydia. She deserved someone better. Bobby saw me at that moment and shouted out, “Hey Twerp, what are you doing in here?” I didn’t know what to say or do, and so I blurted out, “Hi, Bobby.”

I could tell that Lydia was looking at me. I decided to go to the back of the store as if I was looking for something. When I could see that Dad had paid and was ready to go, I hurried out the door without saying goodbye to Lydia.

I was still a twerp. But someday…

11. To become a priest I had to have confidence.

For the next week I spent most of my time dreaming about the Studebaker. It would only be two months until that beauty would be mine. One morning a thought popped into my mind. It was a horrible thought that I had never considered before. Where would I park the car when I wasn't driving around the streets of American Fork with Lydia sitting by me? My family didn't have a garage. Dad parked his truck in the straw barn. But a straw barn wasn't a fit place for something as magnificent as a Studebaker. If I parked it out front by the mail box it wouldn't be safe. We didn't have any car thieves in American Fork, but some honest guy could've been tempted to become a thief if he'd seen a Studebaker sitting right there for the taking. And who could blame a guy for stealing something as great as a Studebaker? Having that car for one night would be worth going to the State Pen for six months.

Finally, I was able to put worrying about where I would park out of my mind by telling myself, "I'll just have to cross that bridge when I come to it."

There was another thing that kept creeping into my mind. This thought was the worst thought that could ever come to any human being. It was the thought that Bobby Jackson was right. Maybe I really was a twerp. I had been growing and getting stronger, but inside I still didn't feel that I was as good as most of the other guys at school. I just didn't have confidence. I knew I had to get more confidence if I was going to be the star on the basketball team. If I was going to make long shot after long shot like Bill Ray Jeffries did, I would have to have confidence. And if I was going to be able to have a lot of personality when I was riding along with Lydia in the Studebaker I would have to have confidence. I would have to be able to tell her jokes and tell her that she was beautiful and put my arm around her. I hated to admit it, but maybe having the best car in town wasn't enough. I had to have the charm to go with it. After stewing for many nights, I decided that maybe if I had the car that would give me the confidence. I hoped so.

Don't get me wrong, there were some times when I would get a strong dose of confidence flooding into my heart. I would feel that I was really important and that I could do anything. But then, after awhile, I would start feeling like I was a nobody again. When I felt that way I hoped I wouldn't see Lydia because I knew I would be afraid to talk to her.

There was one time that I always felt confident. On Sundays at church I felt like I was the king of the world. When I knelt down and blessed the sacrament, something came over me like a warm blanket. When I stood up and passed the trays to the deacons, I felt I was like Peter and those guys in the Bible. I would look out at the people sitting in the congregation and some of them would look at me in a way that I can't describe. It seemed like they were admiring me. I couldn't imagine people admiring me. But, on the other hand, I was a real servant of the Lord. I felt good all during the long meeting. And when the meeting was over I would shake hands with some of the people. I loved all the people at church—even me.

Of course, when the speaker was a bit boring, my mind went wandering off to thoughts of cruising along in my Studebaker. I also thought of how the celery was growing and how proud I was that I took such good care of it. I thought about how I was growing. How I had picked up that hundred pound sprayer and sprayed the whole rest of the field after Delmar had gone down. I wished the bishop would let me go into the Deacons class and tell those young boys that if they wanted to make their dreams come true they would have to work as hard as I did. That they couldn't quit just because the sun was beating down hard on them or because they were so hot and thirsty that they thought they would die. I would tell them they would have to take responsibility like I did. They would have to keep going against great odds like I did. I would tell them that they would have to work from daylight till dark; that they would have to quit swearing like I had quit.

These thoughts made me feel confident. But I wondered if I could hold onto those good feelings.

12. *To become a priest I had to have a tender heart.*

On Monday, Delmar had a doctor's appointment. I was alone with the celery. A few years ago, the Storrs brothers had leveled the whole field off. They did it because there was one part that was higher than the rest. When they scraped the higher part, they took the good soil away and put it down into a lower part. With some of the top soil gone, there were some rocks on the surface in that small part of the field. That part also remained slightly higher than the rest of the field. The combination of the two factors made it hard to get water to the plants in that area. Delmar had, from the beginning, said that we shouldn't even plant there, but I wanted to plant everywhere possible. I wanted the money to be flowing in. So I had personally planted that part. It had been hard to get the plants in the ground there but I had determined that those pants would grow as well as all the rest of the field.

They were doing pretty good. Not as good as the other part, but pretty good. So while Delmar was gone, I was putting extra effort into watering that section.

For some reason I liked that part of the celery field the best. I felt like it was my baby. I didn't tell Delmar or anyone else about the feelings I had about those plants. I had a lot of tender feelings that I kept to myself. I didn't want people thinking that I was a sissy. I wanted to be known as a tough sort of guy. I didn't tell people most of the things that I felt. I never once, at any time, told anybody the way I felt about Lydia. I guess part of that was because I was afraid they would think, "She never thinks of a guy like you, she's way out of your class."

At any rate, I kind of felt like I was a celery plant growing in a poor spot of ground. That was the reason I liked the plants in that part of the field. So whenever I had time, I would go to that place and hoe and pull any weeds that got close. I would give it an extra drenching of insect spray so that no insect like Bobby Jackson could hurt it.

I almost had to defy gravity to get the water to it. But by using my shovel to push it, I could get the water there. I didn't work like that when Delmar was around. It was just when he wasn't there that I did that.

It was now late July and it was getting hot. I usually hated hot weather. But this summer I appreciated the hot sun bearing down on our field of celery. Our celery liked the sun as much as I liked the bacon and eggs that Mom cooked for me every morning.

Summer was passing and nothing could stop us now, or could it?

13. To become a priest I had to be teachable.

On Tuesday, as Delmar and I were working, Stewart came in his truck. I loved it when he came. He always told us what to do to help our celery. I got to thinking that he was a bit like Jesus was. Jesus would tell his apostles how to heal the sick and how to cast out devils and how to love the people. I wasn't the most religious guy in the world, but I never would say the name of Jesus when I was mad. Some guys did that and I knew I would be tougher if I did. But I couldn't do it. I just couldn't say that.

Stewart went right to the head of our field and said, "There is something wrong with your celery."

He acted like he was having a vision as he gazed at our field. He slowly turned his head until it seemed he had looked at every single plant. Then he spoke. "Your celery isn't the right color."

"Green is the right color," I replied.

"There are many shades of green," he replied, "and your celery isn't dark green. If we don't do something to change the color you will lose most of your crop."

I saw the vision of my Studebaker fading fast.

Then he smiled and said, "I can tell by the color that you need to give it more water and then you need to give it a certain amount of fertilizer."

"How do you know?" asked Delmar.

"The Japanese farmers taught me how to read celery. They taught me to look at the color and know just what to do. Your celery will be all right, but tell the Storrs brothers that they need to get you some Ammonium Sulphate, and have it here by tomorrow morning. If you put that on and give it a good watering, with all this sun your field will start to grow an inch a day."

"An inch a day," I said with glee.

"An inch a day," he replied.

I could tell that Delmar liked what he had just heard as much as if he had heard that American Fork was rated to win the state football championship in the fall.

You can bet your life that Delmar and I did everything exactly the way that Stewart had told us. We put the fertilizer down and let the water trickle through it. We made sure every plant got just the right amount. I wished to myself that I could treat everybody the way that we treated our celery. I had never been so concerned about something feeling good as I was about those magnificent plants.

I stayed after Delmar went home and made sure my plants on the high rocky ground got their fair share of food and water. It took a long time but I couldn't let those plants go without.

Two days later the green color had changed into another green color—the right green color.

I knew there was only a month to go and then I could stop dreaming and start reaping the harvest that the dream had promised. I would be rich and popular, and Lydia and I would be the talk of the school. I didn't know at that time what lay between me and my glorious future.

14. To become a priest I had to be able to grow in rocky ground.

I couldn't wait each morning to get back down to our field. We were caught up on the work. It had become more of a waiting game. I just wanted to be there to see the celery grow. I figured I could measure it with my ruler in the morning and then at night I would be able to tell exactly how much it had grown. I got to thinking that if I stared at one plant for an hour, I would actually be able to see it grow an eighth of an inch. I had never been as excited as I was there, watching that beautiful green stuff start reaching into the heavens.

One mid-August afternoon, while Delmar was at football practice, I sat alone with my celery. I shouldn't have called it, "my celery". It was really our celery—Delmar's and mine. But I didn't think that he loved it like I did. I loved it because I had done so much to help it grow, because I had planted it. I loved it because I watered it, and hoed it, and fed it. I loved it because I had saved it from the hoppers. I loved it because I had prayed for it, and sacrificed for it. I was proud of it and felt that it was mine.

As I sat there on the ditch bank it was really quiet. The only sound was some red winged blackbirds that were squawking in the distance. I started to think wonderful things. I started to feel tender feelings. I started to think of how much I loved my dad. I always thought of how much I loved my mom. But I had never thought it about my dad. I knew how much he loved me, and how much he had done for me. I thought, "I'm kind of like the celery and dad is sort of like me. He would do anything for me." I was glad that he was my dad.

I didn't know why I thought that. I had never thought anything like it before.

I got to thinking about love. I loved my celery and I loved my family. And I loved myself. I was shocked at the feelings of love that I had for myself. I spent most of my thoughts about myself wishing that I was somebody else. I had always wished I was like Don Peterson or even my brother Kent. Guys that everybody liked and who everybody knew. Great athletes. But then I thought, "I would sooner be me than them." I was shocked at that realization.

I listened with my right ear really close to one of the plants. I thought I could hear it growing. I could see that the celery was changing. It was taller. In a way it was doing what I was doing. I had grown several inches over the past year, and still had a couple of months before my seventeenth birthday. I wondered if the celery was as happy about growing as I was. I wondered if each plant wanted to be just a little bit taller than the ones next to it.

I was happier about growing than about anything that I had ever done. I wanted to be a basketball player and I knew that growing taller was my only chance. My brother was six feet seven inches tall when he was my age. People would see me and him and say, "George, your brother Kent is a head taller than you. When are you going to grow?" I would say, "I don't know." And I would smile, but inside I wasn't smiling. Inside I was resenting them. They had reminded me of how little I was and made me feel bad about myself. I knew people expected me to be tall and I wasn't. People expected me to be a lot of things that I wasn't. I hated that. In a way I kind of hated myself because I knew I should be a lot of things that I wasn't.

My mind shifted and I started thinking about how the celery would make me a fortune, and I would be everything everybody expected me to be. The celery was becoming what I expected it to be.

It had always been celery. I knew that was what we had planted more than two and a half months earlier. But it hadn't looked like celery then. At first it had looked like a little pencil. After some time it grew more leaves and spread out like a dandelion hugging close to the ground. Then parts of it had grown up until it was like little bush. Finally it started to look like celery.

I thought to myself, "I'm about the same age as this celery. I was little and then I was a bush and now I'm starting to grow. I'm starting to be what Heavenly Father expects me to be."

The celery wasn't just growing taller it was maturing. I was doing that too. My body was really changing. I remembered seeing myself in the mirror that morning. I was still a boy, but I was starting to look like a man. The celery was different now and so was I.

But the celery seemed so much better than me. It didn't worry about things like being popular, or being an athlete, or winning the love of certain plant across the row named Lydia. It just wanted to be a good celery plant and get shipped to New York and be a on a table with a roast turkey and cranberries and have people wishing the prayer on the food was over so that they could take a big bite of the best Thanksgiving treat of all—the celery.

But then I started thinking that I could do better. I could help others and do good things. I could be what my mother always told me that I could be.

I stood up and walked down the closest row. I was careful not to knock even a leaf off. The plants reached up to my knees. They were damp and made my trousers a little wet. They seemed to want to reach out and touch me. I could tell that they liked me. Finally I came to the part where it was rocky--the place where it was hard to get the water. I walked to the very center of this little portion of our giant field. I stood there and it seemed like each plant was so glad that I had come to see them.

It was then that I decided to do something that I hadn't done all summer. I decided to break off just one piece of celery from one of those plants and one from one of the plants where the soil was the richest and then have a taste test. As I had this thought each plant seemed to say, "Take part of me." I broke a piece from one of the closest ones. Then I headed back to the middle of the field where the soil was richest and broke off another stalk.

I went to flowing well and washed each one. I kept the one from the rocky area in my right hand and the other in my left. Then I sat down on the grass and prepared to do a taste test. There is no greater thing to do with your teeth than to let them have the pure joy of crunching though a celery stalk.

Before I took a bite I put a little pinch mark in the small end of the celery stalk that I had picked from the rocky area so that I could tell which one it was.

I took off my straw hat and put the two stalks inside and shook them up. Then without looking I pulled one out. Not knowing which I had picked, I opened my mouth and crunched down. The flavor of celery spread thought my mouth like a tidal wave of freshness. I had never tasted anything so delicious. I chomped and chomped until all the water had gone out of the celery, and filled my whole mouth. I said to my self, "No other celery in the history of the world could be this delicious."

Half of the taste test was done. Certainly that stalk was the best. But which one was it; the rocky soil one or the lush soil one?

Without looking for the mark I picked up the second piece, opened my mouth and crunched down. This one also tasted like celery--delicious celery. But there was something different. This one had a taste that I couldn't ever describe. It seemed to fill not only my mouth with its juice, but also my heart.

It was time to see which celery was the first I had tasted, and which was the second.

I almost decided not to find out. But then I couldn't resist knowing. I found that the first had been last and the last had been first. The last, the most delicious to the taste and heart was the celery from the rocky patch.

I wondered if I was from the rocky patch. I wondered if I could fill someone's heart.

The Studebaker would guarantee that.

I wondered if somewhere, workers were at that minute putting the fenders on my very own Studebaker.

Their work wouldn't be in vain. At least I hoped it wouldn't be.

15. To become a priest I had to learn that the last part is the hardest part.

Normally I didn't want summer to end. But that year, well, that year was a different story. That year when summer ended I knew I would be a rich man. I would own a brand new Studebaker. I would ride along like the wind. Someone would be seated at my side. Who would that be? I'll let you guess. It had been a long ninety days crammed with hard work and worry and hope. And it was nearly over. The scene of black soil had been replaced with an acre and a half of the most beautiful green ever created in heaven or earth. Green! Oh yes green! What a glorious color. Green backs that could be cashed in for the perfect dream.

Finally, the beloved celery was ready to be harvested. It was the time that the real work would begin. Delmar would serve as the foreman of the harvest and I would be second in command. That suited me just fine. He didn't give orders; he just made suggestions and to me those suggestions were orders. I knew he could work harder and lift more than me or any other guy in American Fork. I would forever be grateful for him leading out in making my dream come true.

BECOMING A PRIESTHOOD MAN

On the Monday morning of August 26, 1948 I bounded from my bed with the excitement that's only possible when you're about to have the best day of your life. That was the day we would begin the harvest. I had asked Nerk Conder, Dick Hampton and Orval Jeffs to work for us. We would pay them 50 cents per hour. When I arrived at the field, they were ready to go. Delmar wasn't there yet. I knew that he had stopped off at the Storr's house to pick up the truck. Soon he came down the lane that led to our land. I could see someone riding with him. I didn't recognize who it was at first. But as he drew closer I was stunned to see that it was Bobby Jackson. My perfect day went down the drain. What was he doing here? He jumped out of the truck and greeted me with, "Well if it isn't old Twerp himself."

I could never quite figure out why having him say that caused my insides to turn over. It just seemed to strip me of all the good things that I was trying to build inside myself. The name "Twerp" made me feel that I was everything I didn't want to be. Maybe he was right. Maybe I was a twerp. Maybe Lydia would never like me. She could never like a twerp. A twerp could never be a basketball player or any other kind of an athlete. A twerp could never become a priesthood man like my brother Stewart. I hated Bobby Jackson more than any other human being that I knew. And when he was around I hated myself. What was he doing here?

Delmar announced. "Bobby can help us lift crates to the highest level of the truck. He can also help unload them at the celery plant. So I hired him to give us a hand until the celery is all harvested."

I really resented that Delmar had done that, but I knew that Bobby would be a big help. It was just that he would spoil most of the joy I could've had in doing the most exciting thing I had ever done in my life.

The truck was loaded with forty wooden crates. Delmar shouted, "Okay men, lets get these things unloaded and get started."

A week earlier, Stewart had taken me to the Alpine Hardware to buy six big butcher knives. We had then gone to his shop and cut off the end of the blades so that they were only about five inches long and looked like a chisel. Then we had used a grindstone to sharpen the flat ends of these knives. Then we filed them and really made them sharp. I had brought them with me that morning. I handed them out to the crew. Delmar remarked, "Man George, you sure have done a good job on these knives."

The minute had finally arrived. I felt like we were about to go onto the beaches of Normandy on D Day during World War II. We each knelt at the head of a row. The celery seemed to be eager to be cut from the ground and to begin its journey to New York City.

The way we did the work was by crawling on our knees, taking our chisels, and cutting the celery stalk off just below where it attached to the roots. We took a hold of the celery with our left hand and pushed the knife forward with our right hand and the celery would be free. Then we'd hack off the top leaves, lay the huge plant aside, and go to the next one. The excitement of doing this caused me to forget that Bobby was even there.

The work went a little slow as we got used to the process. But after about an hour we were really moving along.

Delmar and Nerk were putting the celery into the crates and loading them into the truck. We could get about sixteen bunches in each crate. By noon we had the truck almost half loaded. After lunch we were back at it. By two o'clock we had the truck about loaded. It had not been hard to load as long as we could stand on the bed of the truck. But when we reached the last row there was no where to stand on the truck. It had to be lifted up from the ground. Delmar hoisted one up. I decided to try. But before I could Bobby pushed me aside and said, "Give me that. There is no way you could get that up there."

He had a hard time himself, but he finally made it. It was no trouble for Delmar to get them up. He did the last two.

Finally it was time to take our first load to the celery plant. It was about a half mile up the old dirt road and then a few blocks on the paved road.

Delmar tied the load on with a thick rope. He tied a knot in it that really cinched it up. I stood in awe, wondering how he knew how to do all this stuff.

He got in the driver side and Bobby in the passenger seat. The two of them would go unload it and the others of us would continue harvesting.

As Delmar was about to leave I went over to him and said, "Hey, drive real carefully. That stuff is more valuable than gold. Be sure those guys up there make a record that it's our celery and not somebody else's." He smiled and said, "Sure thing. I'll do that."

I watched the truck go up the old rutted road. The celery crates wobbled from side to side but they stayed on. It was time for us to go back to work. We had all gotten better at our technique. Pushing that knife forward time after time made my arm quiver with fatigue. But I couldn't stop to give it a rest. I kept at it. I saw that the others were faltering a little. I knew I had to set an example and so I worked even harder. Soon my arm didn't hurt any more. I could see the muscles in my forearm kind of bulging. It felt good to work harder than I had ever worked before. It was good to be a foreman. It was good to be doing something that I loved. The others began to complain that their arms were sore and that they were getting blisters. I had a blister, but it had burst inside my glove. I didn't tell them about that. I just kept working. I didn't complain. Leaders are not supposed to complain. I told the guys, "Keep at it. You can do it." I had never talked like that to anybody before.

In an hour or so I saw the dust rising up above the corn field to the north and I knew it was Delmar coming back. We kept right on working until he and Bobby got out of the truck. Delmar said, "Good work you guys. You have really cut a lot since we left."

It felt good to have him say that.

We harvested anther truck load that day. I was more tired than I had ever been before. That night Nerk told me he didn't know if his mom would let him come to work the next day. I could tell that he just didn't want to work-- the work was too hard. I told him, "Nerk, we have to have you on our crew. You know how to work. We got to get that celery in. If you come tomorrow I'll buy you a big milkshake tomorrow night at Cooks Ice Cream Parlor." He agreed to come.

Things went on like that all that week. We had harvested about one fourth of our field. I had thought things would've gone faster. I could see why Nerk wanted to quit. I partly wondered if I would have the energy to stick with it until the end. It would take another three weeks. But whenever I began to have doubts I saw, in my mind, Lydia up by the flowing well cheering me on by saying "George! George! George!" Just thinking that would give me new energy. Somehow I worked harder and each day, instead of getting tired and weaker, I got stronger. I was able to cut more celery than Nerk or Dick. We didn't race, but I could tell that I was faster. I could also stay ahead of Orval and he was pretty quick.

But Bobby was the fastest of them all. Or was he?

16. To become a priest I had to win both little and big victories.

On Wednesday, Delmar took a load up to the celery plant, and then went to the high school to practice football for two hours. When he left, Bobby acted like he was in charge. That bothered me because I was in charge. But I didn't want to say anything. Bobby liked to be in charge and he was a good worker. He brought the truck back.

He came over to where I was and watched me. Finally he said, "You're pretty good at that Twerp. I think you're faster than all the other guys. Course you could never keep up with me."

I worked even faster, and I didn't answer him. Pretty soon he was at my side. And I could tell a race was on. I normally wouldn't have raced him. But something came over me and I had to beat him, even when I knew it was impossible. He was as strong as Mountain Man Dean, the wrestler. It was like a boy against a man. But I started going faster than I had ever gone. He was right at my side. I couldn't get ahead of him no matter how hard I tried. Sweat was pouring off my forehead. My throat burned, and I wanted a drink, but I couldn't stop. I could see that he was also sweating.

On and on we went. The others began watching us like they were at the Kentucky Derby. They started to urge us on,

"Come on George! Come on Bobby!" I was about to give up. "What difference did it make?" I asked myself. Then I said to myself, "It makes all the difference." I started going even faster. He kept right at my side. Just when I couldn't go on, I noticed that he was one celery plant behind me. That gave me new energy and I worked even harder. Then he was two behind and then three. Finally he threw his knife in the air and fell on his side. The other guys cheered for me; until he gave them a dark look and they shut right up.

I stood. I didn't want to act proud, but I guess that is the way that I looked because I couldn't help it. I had beaten him. I knew it and he knew it.

He stood up, came over and said, "I could have beaten you by a mile if I had wanted to." I didn't reply. He said, "Do you want to make something of it?" I knew that he knew he had been beaten at celery, but I also knew that he could beat me in another way. He then repeated what he had said many years ago, "Do you want to make something of it?"

I just stood there. I was scared, but I wasn't going to back down.

He looked me in the eyes and I looked him in the eyes. Then he said, "Well do you?" I didn't reply and he came toward me. With rage in his eyes he lunged at me like a bull. I quickly stepped aside, reached over and put a hand on each of his shoulders and thrust him backwards to the hard ground. He fell hard on his back and was in pain. He had also gotten the wind knocked out of him. He gasped until he caught his breath.

Then he jumped up and said, "You'll regret that." This time he came at me with his fists flailing. I could tell that if he hit me I would be out for a week.

I had never been in a real fight. I was scared but somehow I wasn't scared.

During the past school year, Coach Leo Nelson, our gym teacher, had had us box each other. I had been teamed up with Mark Grant. Mark and I were about equal and with the big gloves we never did any harm to each other. But then, between rounds, Coach Nelson called me over and said, "George if you will quit hitting like you're a windmill you could beat him. Just hold your fists right in front of your chin. Then throw your punches straight out." I started in round two against Mark. Doing exactly what Coach Nelson had told me, I hit him, and then I hit him again, and again. He didn't know what to do. I was boxing like a real fighter. Coach Nelson was pleased but Mark wasn't.

So when Bobby came at me with his arms flailing, I was about to do what Coach had told me to do. I put my hand under my chin and was about to fling a right fist straight out to his nose. But instead, I stepped quickly to the side and he went flying by like a race car out of control. He went head first into an empty celery crate and smashed it as flat as a pancake. At first he just laid there real still like he was dead. All of us stood by in a silent shock. Then, after a second or two, to my amazement, Bobby started to laugh. He looked at me and said, "George you got to be the fastest man on earth. Trying to hit you is like trying to hit that Shadow guy on the radio."

I looked at him all crumpled up and laughing. It seemed like the funniest thing I had ever seen. A big smile started spreading across my whole face. I began to laugh with him. I went over, held out my hand, and helped him up. As I looked into his eyes, I felt myself feeling a real good feeling--some how I knew that I had a new friend.

We all walked over to the flowing well to cool down. Bobby told me to go ahead and get the first drink. I think it was his way of honoring what I had done. He told me, "I respect you George."

As he said that, I felt an inward respect for myself. I had finally stood my ground. I almost felt like I could hear the celery plants cheering.

Nobody on the crew ever mentioned that little episode to anyone else. I sure didn't bring it up, and neither did Bobby.

I liked Bobby a lot after that. And he never did call me a twerp again. Instead he always called me, "Big Du."

When we loaded the truck we got to the back row. Bobby said to me, "I'll put two up top, and you can do the other two."

Somehow I didn't have any trouble doing my two.

I'll never forget that time in the celery field. I have never gotten into a fight since. I retired from my boxing career without ever losing a bout.

But there were more important bouts ahead.

17. To become a priest I had to love the planting more than the harvest.

I had never looked forward to anything more than getting that last truck load of celery on the truck and on it's way to the plant. I told Delmar that I wanted to load the last crate in the corner row on the back. After all of the crates were in place, I bent over the last one, picked it up, took a deep breath, and put it up there like it was packed with feathers.

The crew cheered. It was over.

But somehow the end didn't bring the feelings that I had expected. I looked back at the field strewn with celery leaves and debris. Somehow I felt as empty as the field looked. For three months my thoughts had been upon that glorious field. Now it was over. My heart was heavy. I stared longingly towards the truck that was slowly getting smaller and smaller in the distance.

The celery harvest was over. But the fruits of my labors were just beginning. Now all that separated me from my riches, from my car—my Studebaker, and my Lydia was a shipment to New York City. And then it was only a matter of time before the Storrs brothers received the check. Half to them. A fourth to Delmar. And a fourth to me.

With the quality of our celery, I knew I would have enough for the car, for some sharp clothes from Devey's Men Store and for Lydia. No matter how I felt, happy or sad, the very thought of Lydia turned my sadness into happiness or my happiness into pure ecstasy. I looked to Mt Timpanogos and said a silent prayer of gratitude for my success. I felt so good.

I walked slowly across the top of the field. We were nearly into October but the weather on most days was still warm. I was thirsty. I walked toward the flowing well. I closed my eyes, and followed the pleasant sound of life that the water made as it came up from the depths and splashed down into the small pond. I bent over and put my face into the cool refreshment. The water had never tasted so good. I drank several swallows, and then I immersed my whole head into its depth. I lifted my head and shook it like a dog shaking off the water from his back. I loved this well. This would be the last time it would quench my thirst. I would miss the well. I would miss the rich soil. Most of all I would miss my beloved celery.

I walked to Dad's old truck and got in. I backed up and then went forward in a half circle. The field was behind me. I drove away. I didn't look back with my eyes, but I did with my heart. The field, the growing celery had changed my life.

Now it was just a matter of waiting and all my dreams would come true. Or would they?

18. To become a priest I had to know that there are dreams within dreams.

Finally, after a long month, the time came. Stewart called and told Mom that he would come up in fifteen minutes with my money. I sat at the bay window where I could see the corner of 7th North and 2nd East. Soon I knew that Stewart's car would come up the old Alpine Road, turn the corner, and park in front of our old rusty gate.

Two minutes later there he was. I could barely control my emotions. My dream would soon become a reality. The time for waiting had been long, but it was now over. I watched as he came up the walk to the steps of the porch. Before I knew it he was in the room with me. He reached out and handed me an official looking envelope; the kind of envelope that bankers and rich people used.

I sat down in the old rocking chair and began to rip the envelope. Stewart cautioned, "Careful, or you will rip the check." Then there it was. It was just a piece of paper, but oh what a piece of paper. It was like a ticket to my glorious future.

I tried to read the amount but I couldn't for it was upside down. I turned it over and read, "Pay to the order of George Durrant." I couldn't read on because my heart was racing and my hand was shaking. Then I could see the figures $474.27. The check should have read $6,074.27. I knew I had read it wrong. I read it again, $474.27. I looked up at Stewart.

I couldn't hide my disappointment. "Is this just the first check? Will there be more checks?"

"No that is the total. There won't be any more."

"You mean that this is it?" I questioned.

` "That is it. Are you disappointed?"

"I mean all that work. I thought it would be more." I responded.

"It would have been. You raised some great celery. Last year you would have made a lot more. But this year some farmers near New York City decided to raise celery like the kind we grow here. They didn't have to pay the big shipping costs that we pay. That made the price drop way down."

Stewart could sense my deep disappointment. He added, "That is still a lot of money. You can buy a lot with that kind of money."

"Not a car," I muttered.

"You don't need a car. School is just four blocks away."

I didn't try to explain. Stewart was a smart man, but he could never be able to understand. Nobody would ever be able to understand.

Mom came in from hanging clothes on the line. Stewart said to her, "You have a very rich son."

She excitedly asked, "How much did you make George?"

I handed her the check and she read the amount and said, "Wow! That is wonderful! You can pay a lot of tithing on that."

I needed to be alone. I went out the back door, past the woodshed and beyond the barn. There were some trees there. I could be alone there. I needed to be alone to face the sorrow of my shattered dream. I sat on my log, lowered my head into my hands and wondered why. I raised my head and looked upward. I asked out loud, "Why?"

After several minutes, some feelings that I had never felt before came from somewhere and began to settle into the deepest part of me. As I looked up I could see the golden leaves high overhead on the tall trees. I loved these trees which were now dropping their leaves in preparation for the coming winter. I watched one leaf as it fell from a high branch and floated slowly toward the ground. Soon it gently took its place among those that had already fallen. I too had fallen from a high place. I too was now at the bottom.

I was confused. Why did I not feel like I should feel? Where was the sadness? Why did I have a feeling of relief? Like a burden had been lifted--a feeling of joy. Somehow I knew that all would work out. I looked heavenward. I felt I could almost see God. I could feel His love. I whispered, "Thank you."

I stood up and headed home. It had been a good summer. It was good to have a dream. I had never had a dream before. For the first time, I had been a partner with my

Heavenly Father. I had listened with my heart. I had refused to quit. I had gained confidence. I had loved planting and harvesting. I had finished all that I had started.

I was all the way back at the woodshed when it hit me. I remembered a Christmas some six years before. That Christmas I had dreamed of getting a brand new red, purple and white Hiawatha Bicycle. It broke my heart when I didn't get it. But now I could get it. That is what I would do! I would get that bike. I had plenty of money to do that. When I got back inside Mom could tell I was really happy. She asked, "What are you grinning about?"

"Cause my long time dream is about to come true." I replied.

I gave her a big kiss on the cheek and announced, "I'm getting myself a Hiawatha bike. I won't even need a garage for that."

The next day when Gambles Hardware Store opened I was there. Five minutes later I had the most beautiful bike in all of American Fork.

I paid Mr. Gamble, pushed my bike to the sidewalk, stomped down on the peddle, threw my long leg over the bar, sat on the seat and was off. What a thrill! I had waited so long.

I peddled over toward Bradley's Market. That wasn't the direct way home. But that was the way I was drawn. On the way there I passed the basketball coach, Coach Oberly. He shouted, "Hey slow down. We don't want you getting hurt. We got a championship to win."

He had never talked to me like that before. That is the way he talked to his star players. The next person I saw was

Stewart coming out of the People's State Bank. "Great looking bike!" he shouted. He added, "I need to talk to you Sunday after church. The Lord has something special for you to do to help the other priests."

As I rode on I wondered about things. You can do a lot of wondering when you're riding a bike. I wondered, "What does the Lord want me to do?" Whatever it was, I sure would do it.

Then I was at Bradley's Market. I parked my bike carefully against the side of the store. I didn't want to scratch it. I looked up, and there looking out the window was Lydia. She had watched me ride up.

I hurried in the door. As I entered, I shouted, "Hi Lydia." I had never greeted her so boldly before. It was almost like I was telling her that she sure was lucky to be seeing me. I could tell by the look on her face that she felt lucky to be seeing me.

Her Uncle Tom was over cutting meat, and nobody else was in the store. I was there all alone with Lydia. Somehow I wasn't nervous about that. I was feeling really confident. Then I spotted a stalk of celery over in the vegetable display. I walked over and picked it up; that gloriously green bundle. I returned to Lydia. At that moment, I knew what it would be like to enter heaven.

I held the celery up, like it was a big bouquet of flowers, and turned it in my hand as Lydia looked on in admiration. Then I said, "Lydia, what do you know about celery?"

"Not much." She said humbly.

"Well, would you like to know more?"

I knew that no guy from Lehi or anywhere else had ever asked her that before. She seemed speechless. I had never seen her speechless before. She looked so beautiful being speechless. I turned and returned the celery back in its place. I was walking like I was student body president. I came right up to the counter, leaned across towards her and said, "Nice sweater Lydia." Her face went kind of red.

We just looked at each other. The she said, "Nice bike."

"I just bought it over at Gambles. It's a Hiawatha."

"Wow!" she replied as she looked out the window at the bike. Then she looked back at me, "It's a beauty." She acted kind of shy as she said, "I've got a bike."

"Really!" I replied.

It seemed a little like she was as shy as I had used to be as she said, "I finish work here at two o'clock. Would you like to come over and we could ride our bikes down to the mill pond?"

I was confident, but I couldn't take it any more. This was too much for me. I turned and said, "I've got to get home to gather the eggs."

As I went out the door she shouted. "I'll see you at two. I would like to know more about celery."

BECOMING A PRIESTHOOD MAN

Have you ever been on a bike when it seemed like it had a motor? Maybe my bike felt that way because its wheels were not touching the ground. I knew this would be a good year!